CW00664311

the yoga of healing

the yoga of *healing*

swami sivananda radha

with a preface
by swami radhananda

timeless books 2007

timeless books
www.timeless.org
©2007 timeless books

Design by todd stewart www.breeree.com
cover photo by andrea rollefson
This edition is printed in Canada on 100% post consumer waste
   paper that is chlorine and acid free.

Library and Archives Canada Cataloguing in Publication
Radha, Swami Sivananda, 1911–1995.
      The yoga of healing / Swami Sivananda Radha.
ISBN 978-1-932018-17-2
I. Yoga--Therapeutic use. 2. Healing. 3. Mind and body.
I. Title.
B132.S6R33 2007   294.5′436   C2006-906889-5

Also by Swami Sivananda Radha

Light & Vibration: Consciousness, Mysticism & the
    Culmination of Yoga (2007)
The Divine Light Invocation (2006)
Hatha Yoga: The Hidden Language (2006)
Mantras: Words of Power (2005)
When You First Called Me Radha: Poems (2005)
Kundalini Yoga for the West (2004)
Realities of the Dreaming Mind (2004)
Radha: Diary of a Woman's Search (2002)

Timeless Small Book Series

The Devi of Speech: The Goddess in Kundalini Yoga (2005)
The Divine Light Invocation (abridged) (2001)
The Rose Ceremony (2004)

Audio

Relaxation (2002)
Guided Meditation (2002)
Hari Om (1997)
Om Namah Sivaya (1997)
The Power of Mantras (1997)

contents

preface

Being ill is a crisis in our life. We all know how it feels to have an imbalance in our body or our mind, or depression in our spirit. It is a painful situation to be in, mentally, emotionally, physically and spiritually. Sometimes it can be a matter of life and death.

And yet during this crisis, we find ourselves in a decision-making time, a time when something suddenly can get worse or better, an uncertain time when action must be taken. So often when people have confronted a life-threatening illness, they say, "It made me stop and really think about my life." Or, "It changed my life."

Illness is part of our inner guidance system. While there are many technologies and medicines available that can fix us, we can also turn to our inner spiritual resources and ask: What is it that really needs to be healed? In her teachings, Swami Radha emphasized that the path of healing starts with personal reflection and an understanding about whether our pain is self-created or unavoidable. Can you find out what is hurting you? What difficulties are you encountering in your life? What are the messages that arise when you take the time to be caring and attentive to yourself? The key to healing is to not just bandage up the pain, but to reflect on the root cause, treat it and make changes.

In the Tibetan tradition, there is an aspect of the Buddha called the medicine Buddha, who is meditated on to activate self-healing. This Buddha's message is that our body has the capacity to cure itself from ailments. There is a healing spring deep inside that's available, constantly available. It gives us the opportunity to transform our life, to turn it around, to do the inner work and make healing changes. The Buddha's promise is that we can find out what is in disharmony and bring it back into harmony.

Coming back to harmony. What does that mean? Every person is unique, so there is no definite answer, but we can think of it as a sense of well-being, an ability to cope with life's challenges and possibilities, an integration of the good and the bad, the easy and the difficult. We know we are in harmony when we are courageous enough to yield and yet we know where we stand.

The yogic practices are a means of clearing the mind and body, giving us the strength to be ourselves. The practices stretch the mind to incorporate the aid of the Divine forces to help, to inspire, to surround and protect us. The tools available are light, rest, silence, time, movement through the asanas, sound and vibration of Mantra, your own imagination, the power of choice. In the healing process you have time and the space to think of your life, and what your purpose is.

Most people want instant healing results, but the practices are not instant. The practices and reflections are sustaining and designed to mature the positive seeds of Light within into a person who is truly human. It will be natural to be positive. It will be nourishing to be still. Relationships can be harmonious. Inner development is a long-term remedy, and the process of engaging in persevering spiritual practices will benefit ourselves and others.

The world that we are living in now needs healing — the healing qualities of positivity, silence, relaxation, care, compassion and cooperation. We have daily reports in the news of people in pain, hunger and poverty, of killings, sickness and death. When negativity and greed tip the balance, the world becomes an unhealthy place to live, lacking the physical and spiritual resources to care for people. We often feel helpless and separate from the rest of humanity. But remember that we are not separate beings. We can cultivate our emotions, use our intuition and forgive. We need to consciously access the will to bring healing forces into the world in which we live and into ourselves.

Yoga brings us to wholeness. The benefit of coming into health and wholeness through self-awareness is that we stop being just a body — needy, grasping, selfish — and become a living being in the process of gaining wisdom and compassion. This is where we need to develop faith and devotion to seriously be involved with subtle lightness of being. When you do everything in your power to keep your focus on the Light, and bring the Light to each person in your life, then you are being responsible for your health and having a positive effect on others. The more positive view we can have, the more positive effects we can have on the world around us.

The yoga of healing can begin to calm, focus and clear mind to enable us to act from highest ideals. We can start using the knowledge we have with respect and gratitude. In sickness, can we remain there without fear? Can we help and serve others without fear? How are courage and faith established? Can we face death? What is the will to live?

The power in healing is that even though we are in a painful situation, we don't flinch. We incorporate, we embrace. As we live through these experiences we note the pain, our reactions and our resolve to be clear, to learn and do our best in the situation. Whatever we can do to heal keeps the learning positive and supportive. In doing so, we will gain a sense of victory and an understanding of what life is really about.

— Swami Radhananda

part one

a foundation for healing

observing the self

What is it that heals? Is healing a power of the mind? Or of the heart? Or is healing by Divine grace?

There is no simple and direct answer. Illness is an interplay of forces. When healing is needed, it is because there is some sort of disorder in the physical body. The cause of the disorder can be of a variety of natures that we have to clearly investigate. The disorder may be a karmic condition. Or perhaps there are psychological difficulties that cause reflections or disorders in the body, which in time and under certain pressure can become real organic troubles. Sometimes we may make ourselves sick through wrong action or wrong food. Sometimes we simply neglect our bodies.

Remember that pain or illness is not a punishment. That is an oversimplification of our understanding of karma. Healing is a learning process. Sometimes it is an opportunity. You may have to begin with the Light of understanding of the purpose of *your* life, of *your* present condition. Can you let that Light spread into other areas? Can you recognize the Light of compassion, or love? Ask yourself: What do I need to learn from my physical condition? What is the energy that created me in the first place? Where does life come from? Who am I?

Healing is not a hit or miss affair, as it seems to many people. Healing is a situation where we meet ourselves. We meet ourselves.

There is darkness. There is light. I am good, I am bad. I am beautiful, I am ugly. I am healthy and I am sick. Always the pairs of opposites. We move between these polarities, but most of the time they are really only in the mind. In fact, they always start there, and at one point may manifest in the body. But the energy behind these thoughts is neutral. It is so important to remember this, I can't stress it enough. Energy is neutral. If you turn the energy into hate, you have given that colour to the neutral energy. If you turn it into love and compassion, you have given it *that* particular colour.

There is an underlying stream of thoughts that we have to become aware of if we want to help ourselves. And we have to remove as much of the colour as we can. Many diseases and much emotional pain come about through the power of suggestion, which is the result of uncultivated thinking and of habits. The power of suggestion should be thoroughly understood. If you have used self-suggestion in a destructive way, it is very important to bring about this understanding before replacing the old suggestions with new, constructive ones.

The power of positive thinking and the power of negative thinking are a very important pair of opposites to be investigated. Negative thinking exerts such a strong power because of the pushing up of the emotions, which are controlled by the ego. The power of positive thinking needs to get its push from repeated and cultivated visualizations of ideal responses to situations in the mind's eye.

Through watching the mind, we will gradually become aware that the mind interprets everything we experience in reference to ourselves. The awareness comes through the refinement and cultivation of the senses, which are the doors and windows to the world. Such refinement will bring us into more sensitive touch with those around us, because no one is an island. The single cell of the body functions in conjunction with all the other cells, and its very existence depends on the cooperation of all other cells. Similarly, each individual could be compared to a cell in this great cosmic body.

Go beyond the gross sense perception. Perceptions must not be oversimplified. Life is too complex, the human body is too complex, the emotions are too complex, and the mind is too complex, for anyone to dare indulge in oversimplifications. Yoga is very fortunately a process of clarification, and the human tendency of self-centredness, properly applied, can produce marvelous results, and lead us on the path of continuous blessings.

I have emphasized daily reflection many, many times. Reflection means mirroring the events of the day and trying to assess our performance on all levels. Without reflection we would not know when pain is unavoidable or when it is self-created. By our own attitude, we can take situations as helpful or hurtful. Often we are simply inconvenienced, not hurt. If there is an accident, such as cutting our finger, when we are physically hurt, the accident may be due to lack of observation and, therefore, also self-created. Pain has to be recognized as a great teacher.

Record the events of the day — what has happened, what has not happened, but also what you had wanted to happen. What are the actions that have led to becoming upset or emotional? Can you recognize the roots, and cut them off, thereby changing your attitude and allowing for new insights and a new approach? Such a discipline will develop in you an ability to concentrate and to renounce the intruding forces of self-importance and all the other ego manifestations that divide giving and receiving, birth and death, light and darkness.

Through a practice of reflection, we heighten our awareness to the finer perceptions that usually escape us because of the still existing grossness of our senses. In due time, this discipline will help you develop concentration and can lead to the ability to listen to the body, and to develop the perception that the body is, indeed, a spiritual tool.

In the course of your reflections, you may want to ask yourself why you want a spiritual healing or if your expectations of healing are realistic. Would it not be right to have the understanding first? We are always looking for miracles, when we are often quite capable of removing obstacles ourselves.

One of the biggest obstacles to healing is the habit of criticism. If you sit in the judgement seat, you cannot heal. You have to strip yourself of all your resentment. And you have to forgive other people, and then you have to put yourself into the state of grace that you too can be forgiven.

The judge in us is the one that punishes. There is no God in heaven that says, "What have you been doing? Now comes the punishment." No, that isn't it. It is indeed as Jesus said: "The kingdom of heaven is within." In that sense, you are your own judge.

So you have to remove what you know is really wrong. And if your ignorance is cleared, then you have to act according to your new understanding. But you cannot allow yourself to fall back. You learn by trial and error. If you slip, and you say, "Oh, I did it again, and I know better," you regret your actions, and you pull yourself back up, and keep changing. But if you let go and say, "Well, I don't seem to be able to do it," and find all sorts of excuses not to pursue and not to improve yourself, you are training yourself into a belief that you can't do it. Remember your errors and make a decision that you do not want to intentionally repeat your errors, because they do hurt other people.

And if you see how you sometimes fail, and what it feels like when you condemn yourself for your own actions and feel the results of your condemnation about your own actions, you may be ready to forgive others and see their failings with less judgement. Condemnation and discarding wrong actions are two different things. Discriminating between the two is a very important factor in healing.

There may be a concept in your mind that you are not worthy to be healed spiritually, that healing is possible for everybody else but you. Such rejection of healing may not necessarily take place in the conscious mind, but in the subconscious that says, "I am not worthy. I am a sinner, there is no grace, I have to pay." Or "I cannot expect God to forgive and therefore I punish myself with sickness."

Sometimes a person has a negative self-image and says, "Oh, yes, I want to be healed." But underneath there is a strong undercurrent of, "But I'm a terrible sinner, I don't deserve to be healed. It won't work." It's like calling 911 for help but putting the receiver down after it rings only once. Your own concept of yourself is so low that you can almost say there is a hidden power of self-destruction.

You can only heal by seeing the conditions, and by invoking all the compassion you are capable of. How do you become compassionate? Observe yourself, practise awareness, reflect and ask questions in order to gain understanding about yourself. When you see and forgive your own failings, and you are ready to forgive the failings of others, you will have more understanding of healing. Compassion needs an open door of acceptance. That door will open through the Light, the power of the Light, and the very subtleness of the rays of Light.

And we must remember to surrender to God or to the cosmic healing forces, the cosmic power that governs this whole cosmos. The quality of the surrender is related to healing. It takes discipline to renounce what you want to do, renounce your self-will, and truly help, truly forgive. And at that moment, something of that cosmic energy, or Divine Light, can indeed flow through you. But not unless you can surrender to that greater power. The moment there is a slight judgement in your mind – "It was foolish" or "How can anybody do such a thing?" – or any similar thoughts, you will eliminate your capacity to surrender and heal.

Besides the ego's need for attention, which perpetuates illness, and lack of humility, which indicates a wrong attitude, there are many other factors that may interfere when you do spiritual practices for your own healing. You may have a lesson to learn, and so healing may not be what is best for you. You may be eating the wrong food, you may be exposed to a toxic environment, or you may be violating certain laws of nature to which your body is subject. You may also be hurting others without being aware of it and unconsciously punishing yourself for their pain.

The complexity of the human mind and its capacity for pain is so tremendous that we must beware of oversimplification. Pain is a great teacher, but we must understand its message and deal with that before the way is clear for health to be restored.

accessing the body's wisdom

There is wisdom in the cells of the body. There is a wisdom to which the conscious mind apparently has no access. In fact, in Kundalini Yoga we speak of a body-mind, which is not a good translation, but we have to find the closest meaning in our own language. This means the consciousness that is in the body, in all the cells. The body has its own power of knowledge. We have to become aware of that power.

Knowledge comes slowly, by degrees. We have to grow in understanding. The Light of understanding is not a sudden beam that blinds you. The Light of understanding adjusts itself, like your eyes do because they cannot take too much light at once.

So, if you really work with one spiritual practice — combining the physical, mental and emotional — and you try to understand every single experience you have with it, you can move on to even higher levels of insight and understanding about yourself.

Compassion and the creation of inner Light are, from my own experience, *the* major factors in healing. There are schools of thought that say that you can establish or awaken the healing forces only by living a pure life. But we must be careful when we use the word purity, because purity, according to social status, to race, to culture, is very differently defined. If we don't develop Light and compassion, I doubt that even the most "pure" person would be able to truly heal. So rather, ask can we bring the Light into our food? Can we see that cosmic energy in another person? Can the Divine in us salute the Divine in the other? Is it possible to salute the Divine in each other in the most intimate and secret moments? Can we bring that Light into every aspect of our life?

Let the Light come into your life, into every cell of your body, into every level of your emotions, into every level of your feelings, into every level of your thinking, into every level of your intellect. Identify with nothing but your Higher Self. If you are only sentimental about pain, then you cannot help yourself, and you cannot help anyone else.

Included here are numerous yogic practices that may help you on your healing journey. And the healing may not take place the way you think it should. But you leave that to the Divine. These practices are what I call spiritual gifts. And if you treasure them, they will work with you. But they will not work for you. You cannot tell the Divine what to do.

Hari Om.

part two
the healing practices

I am created by Divine Light.
I am sustained by Divine Light.
I am protected by Divine Light.
I am surrounded by Divine Light.
I am ever growing into Divine Light.

the divine light invocation

The Divine Light Invocation aims at activating the healing forces latent within every one of us. It brings Light to all levels of consciousness, emphasizing the positive side of our nature and taking energy away from the negative — the resentments, complaints and self-pity we hang onto and identify with. Sort out the positive and the negative within yourself. Give emphasis to the positive, go beyond your past mistakes and future fantasies, and fill the mind with positive images.

All of us have a certain amount of healing power within our own bodies. Light is a symbol for the force that heals. By seeing yourself and others in the Light you will mobilize those invisible forces that are the gift and property of every human being. The Light can heal us.

Your practice of the Divine Light Invocation will act as an efficient therapy in three main ways:

Physically: It will have a positive effect on your health because the Light is a healing and regenerating force. By thinking of the Light and by identifying with the Light you stimulate the sustaining and energizing forces within the body. By changing your habitual physical and mental posture, even for a short time, your internal processes are beneficially reactivated.

Mentally: By inviting the activity and influence of the Divine Light, you can restore mental balance and establish a sense of proportion and perspective in your affairs. Working and identifying with the Light helps to dissolve negative thought patterns by emphasizing the positive image of Light.

Spiritually: The mind is trained to understand and perceive the reality and all-pervasiveness of higher forces, of cosmic energy in the form of Divine Light. In the light of this new understanding and growth, identification with the Light is seen to be a basic truth common to all religions.

The Divine Light Invocation will help bring you into balance and break the hypnotic condition of identification with the body. Many people choose to indulge in physical gratifications, to remain identified with their bodies and that level of consciousness. Realize that you are not the body, not the mind. With persistent practice the Light Invocation will help loosen mental rigidity and overcome identification with the mind. The Light is always available to you, and you can make yourself available to it. The choice is up to you.

Some healing is instantaneous, but more often the Divine Light Invocation must be done repeatedly over an extended period of time before results are seen. Medical advice and treatment should be sought if necessary, and the doctor should be seen as a channel for the Light.

Help yourself and others to unfold according to the divine plan. See the Light as helping open you or the person you wish to help to a greater understanding and acceptance of God's will and healing grace. Sometimes a spontaneous healing can come simply to show an individual that there is some truth in these things. But it is very serious if the person does not follow this up by changing his or her life.

Through the Divine Light Invocation you can help without telling the Divine what to do. You can't say, "I want to be healthy. I want my friend to get better. I want my mother to be healed. I want my child to be well." It is not up to you. You do not know what is best for any individual. I do not attach any hopes or desires to the Light Invocation and say, "She must get well." The Divine Light Invocation will do for the person whatever that person needs — and still be within the will of God.

See yourself as a channel for the Light, through which the healing force can flow. Do not consider yourself a healer. It is the Light that heals. Imagine yourself as a channel, giving support and direction to the Light, just as a wire channels the electricity flowing through it.

Know that the more you give, the more you receive. Be grateful. Gratitude is one of our finest feelings. If properly cultivated, gratitude will bring many blessings. As channels for the Light we are blessed as much as those to whom we give the Light. When you practise the Divine Light Invocation always express your thanks at the end, on behalf of yourself and those who have received the Light.

practising the divine light invocation

instructions for the divine light invocation

Stand erect, feet shoulder-width apart.

Keep the eyes closed and focus them on the
space between the eyebrows.

Lift the arms above the head at the same time
as you smoothly and gradually tense the
whole body, while you inhale. The arms
should be kept straight and the tension
maintained throughout the body. (*fig. 1.*)

Hold the tension and the breath.

Make the following affirmation to yourself,
silently and with all the concentration
possible:

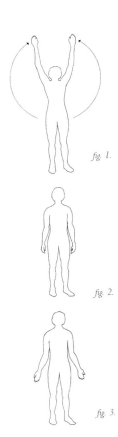

fig. 1.

fig. 2.

fig. 3.

42 the yoga of healing

I am created by Divine Light.
I am sustained by Divine Light.
I am protected by Divine Light.
I am surrounded by Divine Light.
I am ever growing into Divine Light.

Then slowly lower the arms as you exhale and relax.
Keep the eyes closed and use your imagination to
    see yourself standing in a shower of brilliant
    white Light.
See the Light pouring down upon you, flowing
    into the body through the top of the head,
    filling your entire being.
Now, without raising the arms, keeping them at
    your side, tense the body and inhale (*fig. 2.*).
Hold the tension and the breath.
Mentally repeat the Invocation:

I am created by Divine Light.
I am sustained by Divine Light.
I am protected by Divine Light.
I am surrounded by Divine Light.
I am ever growing into Divine Light.

the divine light invocation 43

Slowly exhale and relax.

With the arms beside the body, concentrate on
feeling a warm glow of Light suffuse your
entire body, outside as well as inside.

·Acknowledge silently to yourself:

Every cell of this, my physical body,
is filled with Divine Light.
Every level of consciousness
is illumined with Divine Light.
Divine Light penetrates every single cell of my being,
every level of consciousness.
I have become a channel of pure Light.
I am one with the Light.

The Divine Light Invocation is an exercise of
will as well as an act of surrender.

Be receptive to the Light and accept that you
are now a channel of Divine Light.

Express your gratitude with deep feeling.

Have the desire to share this gift with someone
whom you wish to help.

Turn your palms forward (*fig. 3.*).

You can now share the Divine Light with any
friend or relative. Keep the eyes closed and
visualize him or her standing before you.
Mentally open the doors of your heart centre
and let the Light stream forth toward the
feet of this person.
See the Light encircling the person and
spiraling upward in a clockwise direction,
enveloping the body completely.
See the spiral moving high up into the sky,
taking his or her image along with it.
Finally the person merges into the source of
the Light and becomes one with the Light.
You may even lift your head to follow the spiral
of Light, keeping the eyes closed.
When the person has passed from your view,
relax and silently give thanks for having the
opportunity to help someone in need.
You are now ready to begin all over again,
putting others into the Light, one by one,
in the same way. As you become more
familiar with the Invocation, you may take
several people in a group or a family

together. If you should want to help many
people, you must repeat the complete
Divine Light Invocation as soon as you
notice that your attention begins to slacken.

reflections

1   What needs to be healed?

2   List the resentments, complaints and
     self-pity you have. Do the Divine Light
     Invocation, and see them dissolving into
     the Light.

3   Who am I? What do I identify with? What
     kind of internal effort, the "effort of life,"
     is required to heal?

4   Wrap yourself in a cocoon of Light before
     sleeping. Do the complete Divine Light
     Invocation and spin a cocoon of Light
     around your bed. Then you can slide into

that cocoon of Light as you slide under
the covers.

5   Do the Divine Light Invocation and then
     move into a sitting position. See the Light
     continuing to flow into you. Feel yourself
     absorbing the Light. What insights come
     to you?

6   Sit and see brilliant white Light filling your
     spiritual heart centre. Open to a sense of
     generosity and ask: What am I grateful for?
     Desire to give generously to someone in
     need. Know the more you give, the more
     you receive.

Hari Om

Hari Om

Hari Om

Hari Om

Hari Om

Hari Om

Hari Om

Hari Om

mantra yoga

By chanting mantra or praying with single-pointedness of mind, by reinforcing that concentration with action, by directing the will, healing will take place naturally within ourselves. Mantras can have a healing effect by releasing the emotions and bringing about a state of calmness and deep relaxation both in the chanter and in anyone listening. With the mind relaxed, the source of the disease and the hidden roots of conflict may come to the surface where they can be dealt with. But we must know why we want to be healthy, what we will do with the remainder of life if health is restored. We must be single-pointed in our desire. There may be advantages to being ill that, although we might not admit them consciously, our ego wants to hold onto. By enforcing our will and giving strength to that part that wants to be well, this polarity of the mind can be overcome, permitting healing to take place.

There is a mantra, *Aham Brahmasmi*, which means "I am Brahman" or "I am God." This may seem a strange thought, but a person becomes what she or he thinks. If you think you are a failure, you will become a failure. Conversely, if you continually chant *Aham Brahmasmi*, you will eventually realize your Divine nature and there will be little room for sickness at any level — physical, emotional or mental. If you are to chant this mantra, it is important that you clarify in your own mind what the meaning of God is to you. You must develop the ability to surrender to the mantra and to the energy that comes from it. You must have the humility to be able to ask for forgiveness and apologize to others if you are in the wrong.

When you chant or recite a mantra for someone, visualize that person well and healthy. Do not picture the individual in a sick state, as such an image has remarkable power. Instead, invoke the image of Tara or Krishna or Siva or Jesus and see the person standing in the radiance of Light. Let the healing force flow through you, never from you, and think of the energy of the mantra as that healing Light. Wrap the individual in a spiral of this Light so that he or she becomes barely visible and let the image of this spiral move to the source of all Light. Now focus all your attention on the chanting.

If you have spoken negatively of someone, you can undo the negativity by quickly chanting a mantra and surrounding the person with Light and with the power of the mantra. Ask that your weakness not affect the person and ask to be forgiven. As you become more aware in the moment, you can withdraw what you have said by saying to those who have heard it, "Please forget I said that. It is only a one-sided view."

You can also use mantra to help people you don't know. When you hear a fire or ambulance siren, for example, say, "*Om Namah Sivaya.* Somebody is in need. Let there be help." If you see pictures in magazines or on television of people killed or injured in war zones, put them in the Light with mantra.

When you chant for others, be sure that you are acting out of compassion and not just sympathy. Be aware of any desire to influence the outcome or any strong emotional response. You must keep your own will out of the way, surrendering to the power of the mantra.

When you attempt to heal someone, first invoke all the feeling of compassion possible. Put the sick person at ease, helping that person to accept himself or herself without the feeling of being burdened with sin. Healing will not take place with the attitude of "unworthy sinner." Chant the mantra, and fill yourself with its vibration, thus attracting the forces of the mantra and channeling them toward the sick person. You can mentally open the doors of your heart and let the vibration flow through. With this vibration flows your own love. It is evidence of your willingness to help.

Confidence will come with success, but do not become overconfident and think that healing will always take place. The mantra can overcome anything if the person recites it or receives it as a paying off of karma, with trust in forgiveness and a readiness to alter the course of his or her life, dedicating it to the service of God. However, even when a healing has come about, the sickness may return with greater force if the person who was healed does not change a selfish or hurtful way of life. Gratitude to the Divine must be shown in charity or selfless service to others.

practising mantra yoga

hari om: the healing mantra

Hari Om is the healing mantra. Hari is a name for Vishnu, the preserving aspect of the Divine. Krishna is also an aspect of the preserving or sustaining force, and so Hari may be thought of as the healing aspect of Lord Krishna. God assumes many aspects in order to provide us with a variety of ways to tackle our difficulties, according to individual characteristics and temperament.

In Sanskrit, *Hari* means "to take away." Vishnu takes away the consequences of offences, errors and follies, when there is repentance. These are the impurities that bring about grief and sickness. If they are removed, health and strength are conserved for spiritual endeavours.

Om or AUM is the Hindu trinity, which here means

creation, preservation and destruction: the generation within us of that which is pure, sacred and noble; the sustaining and strengthening of these qualities; and the dissolving of all that is impure and negative. This mantra calls on Vishnu (or Lord Krishna) to preserve the human body and the mind in the best state of health for the purpose of finding Self-Realization, attaining to the Om, the cosmic concept that absorbs all aspects in One, finally becoming formless.

Since the science of sound and breath control applies to any religion, Christians can chant Jesus

Christ to the tune of Hari Om, while Jews can use Adonai or Elohim. A Buddhist might choose one of the names of Lord Buddha; or you can chant the words Divine Mother, or use any one of her 108 names, such as Radha, Laksmi or Saraswati.

When a spontaneous feeling of gratitude wells up toward your teacher or guru, this may be expressed by using the teacher's name as a way of blessing and giving thanks for all that has been received. You can go from one to another of these names, in order to give greater variety to the chanting, without changing the notes and the key in which the mantra is sung.

the mantra so ham — ham sa

Practice of this mantra as described will establish a rhythm in harmony with the rhythm of all the life force around you. A great inner stillness is the result of this practice. This mantra can also be used preceding the performance of the Divine Light Invocation.

Results in all practices seem to be very far away, perhaps even impossible to attain. Do not let this affect you. Remember that only half of the moon is visible at times and yet the light of the moon is always there. It is only that it is obscured from view.

When you begin to do this exercise, use your fingers to count. In time, the rhythm will become a natural flow. The meaning of *So ham* is "I am He" and *Sa ham* is "I am She."

Exhale – mentally repeat So or Sa.

Inhale – mentally repeat Ham.

Repeat this for a few minutes and then reverse, mentally saying Ham on exhalation and So or Sa on inhalation.

the divine light invocation mantra

I am created by Divine Light.
I am sustained by Divine Light.
I am protected by Divine Light.
I am surrounded by Divine Light.
I am ever growing into Divine Light.

The Divine Light Invocation may also be used as a mantra. Repeat the words of the Invocation to yourself and see yourself surrounded by Divine Light in your daily life. It will help you to keep in touch with the Light within you and to see the Light in others around you.

Reflect upon each line of the mantra, each word of the mantra. What do they mean to you? If the mantra is just some words that you say mechanically, that's not good enough. You have to clarify the meaning for yourself as best you can, and on more than an intellectual level – on a level that goes beyond the words. Feelings and emotions must also be involved. It must not be an empty repetition, even though in the course of many years this also would bear fruit.

It's like a tree: if you don't water it, the fruit may be small, undeveloped and dry. But when you take care of a tree and give it water, the fruit comes out in its season, ripe and juicy. Whatever you put into an endeavour, that is what you will get out of it.

reflections

1   Chant AUM. First, chant A-a-a-a-a, placing
    your hands at your navel. How does your
    voice sound? Can you feel the vibration in
    your body? Chant U with your hands at
    your heart centre. Chant M with your
    hands at your throat. Notice your voice
    and the vibrations. Put the sounds A-U-M
    together while placing hands at each
    location. Keep the breath consistent and
    equal for each part. Note how your body
    and mind respond.

2   What is the meaning of the Divine/God
    to you? Close your eyes, focus on the space
    between your eyebrows and visualize your
    image of the Divine. What is the form you
    see? What qualities does your Divine image
    possess? In your mind, approach the Divine
    and ask for a blessing.

3   Chant a mantra, placing down your burdens at the feet of your Divine image. Are there people you may have harmed in the past? Ask for forgiveness and apologize.

4   Prepare a prayer list of people you would like to chant or recite a mantra for. How do you invoke a feeling of compassion? Listen to your voice; open your heart.

5   What is the most important goal for you in this life? What obstacles do you face? What changes do you need to make? What makes your life worth living?

What is the reason you want to be healthy?

What do you need a healthy body for?

What do you want to do with it?

Where do you want to go?

What is the meaning of being alive?

hatha yoga

The meaning of yoga is "union," the bringing together of the various polarities within, in order to reach a state of balance and transcend our limited vision. But Truth is approached by degrees. We have first to know the truth about ourselves. We have learned to cover up our many fears very well. In Hatha Yoga we confront our fears as well as our potentials by balancing attention between the body and the mind. For example, a person who has a neck and shoulders as unyielding as a piece of steel is probably unyielding in daily life. Asanas might loosen up the neck and shoulders temporarily, but becoming aware of the psychological implications will help to make the change more permanent.

Hatha Yoga is a human science that takes into consideration bodily pains, poor posture, faulty breathing and incorrect walking, teaching greater awareness of the body as a whole, without separating it from the mind and the influences of all the senses.

Asanas are a discipline of the body, but they are not without an effect on the mind; and, in turn, the mind affects the body. This interdependency needs to be considered. Individuals must accept full responsibility for their mental-emotional reactions, as well as for the development of their body. This is emphasized in the traditional Hatha Yoga texts. All teachers have stressed the need for a good balance in order to become a well-developed person.

Through the practice of asanas, students will become aware of stress in the body and, by the use of their own minds, discover many of their problems. Changes can then be made in life by a conscious decision on the basis of will and self-analysis. The inability to cope with stress, and the sense of helplessness and hopelessness that many people experience, can be counteracted by recognizing the options and applying the power of choice.

Most people approach Hatha Yoga simply for health. What is the reason you want to be healthy? What is the purpose of living? What is the meaning of being alive? What is your duty? What do you need a healthy body for? Is it to continue having fun, to continue your selfishness and self-importance? That is the wrong reason. You have to assess your life: What do you want to do with it? Where do you want to go?

The first step is to clarify what kind of a person you want to be. What kind of a person do you want to be physically? If you want to be healthy, that is fine, but what about being healthy mentally, emotionally and spiritually? By spiritually, I mean how you personally understand that word. Does it mean something greater than you are? Can you call it Light or inner being or the Absolute? The words don't matter so long as you know what you mean.

The next step is to ask what makes your life worth living. Define that and think about it. And then clarify how you will get there.

The asanas by themselves in the first stage definitely benefit our health. Our muscles get stronger, we become more body-conscious, we sit straighter, we have a different attitude, we give our bodies more balance and rest. Our whole digestive system may respond better and the heart may become stronger. But there it ends unless it is understood that the asanas are meant to be stepping-stones to higher consciousness.

Yoga means that two worlds are being united: the world of the body and the world of the mind in the centre of consciousness. That centre of the mind has to become the magnet to attract the great Light that Consciousness can give, and the body then can become a spiritual tool.

practising hatha yoga

savasana: the corpse pose

The influence of this asana on the body and the mind — from relaxation, to surrender, to death, and even after death — is incredible. If you do not want to be a living corpse, then the purpose of life has to be established. If you want to be an active participant in your life and not a parasite, then the dynamic interdependence between life and death has to be recognized, and the two have to meet in directed and concentrated interaction.

How long has anybody to live? Who knows? What about life that has not yet been lived? What appreciation is there for life and what it has to offer? Is death the great and grim reaper? Or the reliever of pain? Is death the end of all? Is there more than one life? Is death a time of rest between lives, like the night between days?

Throughout life, small but significant warnings appear that are usually disregarded. Loss of physical strength, of sight and hearing, and stiffness in some limbs of the body remind us of our mortality. How are we using the time that remains? If we could only overcome the most merciless master, the ego, life would be dynamic. That is what Saint Paul meant when he said, "Daily I die." After the demands of ego and its greed are surrendered, the struggle for fulfillment of personal desires lessens; life takes on a new zest like a breath of fresh air.

In Savasana, relaxation is the first attempt to surrender, to let go. As the mind follows the flow of the breath, the ripples of the mental lake slowly subside. With continued practice, the senses are gradually withdrawn and become still. Surrender is an essential action for anyone who wishes to lead a spiritual life.

When practising Savasana, passion, egocentricity and self-importance, are, for the moment, put to rest. Rest becomes an important word whose meaning expands with experience. Savasana, the Corpse posture, gives a new understanding of death, of the need for surrender. The body at rest can do its repair work. Sufficient rest allows the body to recuperate from the driving forces of the emotions and the ambitions of the mind. The benefits — physically, mentally, emotionally — are profound. In that state of peace and quiet and inner harmony, one can perceive a vision of the Light that is present in both life and death.

In the quietness of this asana, with eyes closed to shut off all impulses, we open ourselves to the inner forces that give us renewed strength and inspiration to continue on the Path.

instructions for savasana

In this pose, the body lies on the floor face-up and completely relaxed, while the mind is alert. The eyes are closed, the arms at the sides with the palms up. The body remains as motionless as a corpse.

As you work with Savasana, completely relax the body. Observe how the physical position relates to the symbol of the Corpse. Keep your awareness alive through observing, feeling and looking within. Take stock of what is happening physically, emotionally, psychologically and spiritually.

reflections

Focus on one of the following questions while in the Corpse. Move in and out of the pose, letting thoughts, body awareness and insights arise.

1   How long have I to live? Are there parts of my life that have not yet been lived?

2   What appreciation do I have for life and what it has to offer?

3   What would happen if I were to stop the mind's deadly games that kill the goodness in me, the best of my qualities? What would it mean to put to death all the interfering personality aspects that masquerade, deceive and mislead?

4   A dead body no longer resists. Think about
    the energy you put into resistance. In
    Savasana, relaxation is the first attempt to
    surrender, to let go. As you practise
    Savasana, observe the feeling of no
    resistance, of surrender. What is your
    experience?

5   Ask yourself: Why do I want to be healthy?
    How do I want to use the time that
    remains?

Prana is consciousness,
the most subtle life essence
that pervades all manifested forms.
Prana is the sum total
of all existing energy in the universe,
that primal Energy manifest,
unmanifest or in a nuclear state.

pranayama

When we talk about healing, we have to look at breath very specifically. Breath and healing cannot be separated.

Breath is a vehicle of prana. Prana is the life force, it cannot be seen. Breath can only be seen under certain circumstances, but you do not need to be convinced that you breathe. You know that you can't exist without it. You can go without food for a long time, but you cannot go without breath for a long time. It's a fact that you are so familiar with, you take it for granted.

If there is a shortness of breath, there could be an illness. There can be lung trouble, or of the bronchi, some trouble coughing. There can also be heart trouble, there can be undeveloped muscles. And foul breath indicates there is something wrong in the body. If you are breathless, you have been rushing. And holding your breath indicates all sorts of things: tension, anxiety, but also you can be overawed. So you can see that both physical symptoms and emotional responses are expressed in your breath.

You breathe differently if you have a sense of gratitude or humility. If you are in a well-balanced state, your breath is also balanced. You can make a conscious effort to balance your breath.

As the breath is essential to body, take breath as a symbol for cosmic energy. Prana is consciousness, the most subtle life essence that pervades all manifested forms. Prana is the sum total of all existing energy in the universe, that primal Energy manifest, unmanifest or in a nuclear state.

Pranayama is the yogic practice of breath control, which enables us to attune to the cosmic rhythm. It is a process through which we can isolate our inner Self from the influences and influx of mechanical thoughts. Through the practice of pranayama we can gain control over the central nervous system and, most important, over the mind itself.

The yogis teach that we have only so many breaths in each lifetime. An emotional temperament will "burn one up" and thus shorten one's life span. Practice of pranayama leads to emotional control and limitation of selfish desires, so the mind is prepared for the higher stages of yogic practice.

Practising breath control also increases the alpha waves in the brain. If done correctly, it leads to control over the emotions, calmness of mind, curing of nervous disorders and the refinement of sense perceptions. Awareness of the internal noises of the body and other finer, subtler sense perceptions develop. All impurities of selfish desire are removed and a sense of peace and harmony is experienced, which naturally leads the mind to meditation. The mind becomes the abode of extrasensory perception. Intuitive knowledge increases.

Some of the benefits of pranayama are:

Karma can be burned up.

Illusion is destroyed (latent fire in the mind).

Calmness and one-pointedness of mind are
    attained.

Vagus nerves are brought under control.

Proper elimination of carbon dioxide; proper
    absorption of oxygen.

Control over the restless mind.
Sense of peace and harmony.
Increased awareness and ability to observe.
Relaxing effect on the heart and nervous
system.

practicing pranayama

pranayama: preparatory relaxation exercises

Relaxation is essential in pranayama. This is a very important point. Preliminary exercises for the body as a whole, and the neck and shoulders in particular, should be done prior to practice.

1   Neck
Stick head out; pull head back.
Gently drop head to right shoulder; gently
    drop head to left shoulder.
Gently drop head forward; gently drop head
    backward.
Gently roll head in a full circle clockwise, 10 times.
Gently roll head in a full circle counter-
    clockwise, 10 times.

2   Abdomen

Stand with feet shoulder-width apart. Place
    hands on hip joints.
Slightly bend the knees.
Bend forward from hip joints with straight spine.
Pull abdominal muscles in.
Relax abdominal muscles.
Take a deep breath and stretch at the same time,
    lifting arms up.
Exhale, relax arms.
Repeat 10 times.

pranayama: simple 4-4

Bring your body to a relaxed and comfortable sitting
position. Breathe in an even rhythm to the count
of 4. Inhale, 1-2-3-4, exhale, 1-2-3-4. Breathe to this
even count for 10 minutes.

pranayama: 4-16-8 with finger counting

Any sitting pose in which the spine is straight, chin
slightly in and the body relaxed, may be used. The

lungs should be filled three-quarters full without tension and with complete relaxation in the body. In the beginning, do only the practice of 4-16-8 pranayama with finger counting, no more than six rounds daily for the first six months. Do not attempt too much at one time. Always breathe through the nose.

The ideal time for pranayama practice is after Hatha Yoga asanas and end relaxation or Savasana. Take time to relax after each pranayama. Pranayama should not be done by people with high blood pressure.

Below are the instructions for the basic 4-16-8 pranayama, in which one inhales for the count of 4, holds the breath for the count of 16, and exhales for the count of 8. Finger counting is done in pranayama so the mind can concentrate on something else, such as a mantra or short prayer.

1. Inhale for count of 4: Start on left hand with the little finger and continue to left forefinger.

2. Hold for count of 16: Start on right hand with the little finger and continue to right

forefinger (count of 4). Then continue
from left forefinger to left little finger
(another count of 4), making a total of 8.
Repeat this for a count of 16.

3   Exhale for count of 8: Begin on right hand
with little finger and continue to left little
finger for a total of 8.

reflections

1   The mind is affected by the breath. Watch
your mind. Breathe to an even count for 10
minutes. Note what happens with the
mind and emotions.

2   During your pranayama, breathe into a sore
or painful spot in your body. Note what
happens when the breath activates that area.

3   Choose a positive thought or mantra.
Mantra repetition during pranayama

favourably influences the subconscious, giving spiritual suggestion to the mind. For example, with each inhalation breathe in Light; with each exhalation repeat the Divine Light mantra. Note the effect on your mind.

4   Speech depends on breath. Watch your speech — loud, soft, mumbled, abrupt, melodious. Watch your speech during the day. What do you want to use your speech to convey? We are responsible for the currents we set in motion.

5   Breath is our connection to life. How do you express your reverence for life?

See a small stream of white Light
flowing down the centre of your body,
filling the feet, legs, trunk, arms, neck and head.
This form that you call your body
is now a mass of Light.

meditation & visualization

Intuitive perception can be developed by listening within. When one listens, all mental talk has to cease – this is the true meditation state. This is not to be confused with what we in the West term a state of trance, into which it is possible to slip at a certain stage of intense concentration. In meditation the mind is meant to be absolutely alert, even while it is occupied with something else.

It is like a lover sitting on a bench in the park reading a book and understanding what is read, but at the same time having an inner alertness for the arrival of the beloved because the beloved is expected to come. The listening is somehow intuitively tuned in to recognizing the footsteps or the rustling of clothes, something that will announce the presence of the beloved. Immediately this is heard, the lover who waits is alert and ready to receive the beloved.

Visualization is invoking an image or directing imagination. Undirected imagination is only daydreaming and has no results. Concentration exercises are to be done in an alert yet relaxed manner for maximum results.

When you begin to meditate, there are steps you can take to train the mind. For example, select a number of different objects. Concentrate on each one for 3 minutes. It will take practice to achieve unbroken concentration for this length of time. The objects must vary in kind. For example, a piece of wood, glass or bowl of water, a picture of a known person and of an unknown person, a likeable and an ugly one, a picture of a bird, an insect, a fierce animal, a sweet little kitten or puppy.

You can also practise sitting still for 10 minutes watching the mind, then note all that is observed — the emerging images, the thought associations, the distinguishing between concrete and abstract information and the influence of either concrete or abstract images.

Then increase the time by 5 minutes — expand to a half hour and finally to an hour. (This can be done in two ways — first, at the start, every 10 minutes until an hour is complete, watch and take notes. However, the exercise must finally lead into watching the mind for an unbroken half or full hour, with taking notes to follow.) All notes from watching the mind should be compared. If certain aspects repeat, indicating a possible problem, this should be dealt with by continuous questioning.

These exercises will, in time, show how the mind works on all sorts of stimuli presented to it and how the mind is being stimulated apparently from nowhere. Watch what happens if, by old habit, you let the stimuli manifest or, by the new discipline of the mind, you "weed" them out as soon as they appear as thoughts. It is like a million seeds so small they are barely visible, all "sprouting" at once. This process occurs so fast that the earnest aspirant can barely distinguish them. But when control has been achieved, those thoughts die quickly and energy can be diverted toward only the desirable ones. This practice takes care of the innate restlessness that prevents focusing on a single thought or object. The mind can now become a container, open and receptive.

Keeping notes makes it possible to practise recall and to check the accuracy of what you recall. The result of this exercise is a strengthening of memory and, more important, the acquiring of a keen sense of discrimination.

Having learned to concentrate, to recall and to empty the mind, meditation can be attempted because the mind is now like a vessel, able to receive thoughts of a Divine nature. In the beginning there may be insights of great significance, but as soon as intuition begins to unfold, the perceptions are of a different quality, which can be designated as Divine. These perceptions flow into the mind and are often preceded by waves of brilliant hues of blue colour. The meditating aspirant is enveloped in an all-encompassing feeling of peace and harmony. This by itself will become an important stimulus to keep up a regular practice. Soon it will be more than a stimulus; a deep longing will be created within the heart. A sense of peace may come.

practising meditation & visualization

visualizing the body as Light

1   Sit in a meditation posture, cross-legged or
    with your ankles crossed. Rest your hands,
    palms up, on your lap. (As an alternate
    posture, you may stand.)

2   Focus your eyes on the space between your
    eyebrows.

3   Try to think of yourself without the body
    or face; in other words, avoid the familiar
    reflection seen in the mirror.

4   Visualize your body as empty or hollow
    like a glass bottle.

5   See a small stream of white Light (the size
    of a thread) flowing down the centre of this
    glass form, filling the feet, legs, trunk, arms,
    neck and head.

6   Soon you cannot distinguish detailed limbs.
    This form that you call your body is now a
    mass of Light.

7   Hold this image (a mass of Light in the
    shape of your body) as long as possible.
    Repeat often until it becomes familiar.

meditation on the Light

Sit in a comfortable position or in any yogic posture,
but with your ankles crossed. Close your eyes;
focus them on the space between the eyebrows. Do not
start until your body is quiet (perhaps with the help of
a little pranayama).

Become spine conscious. Feel your spine and as
you straighten it out, putting vertebra on vertebra, see
at the base of your spine a Lotus bud slowly open and,

like a dewdrop, a tiny pinpoint of Light slowly
emerging from it, floating in the very centre of the
spine, in that hollow part, up and up and up, passing
through the respective places of the other Lotuses,
finally floating to the place where the spine joins the
head. And in a gentle curve (like a shepherd's crook)
this tiny pinpoint of Light floats over the pituitary and
pineal. In your mind's eye, see a flash of Light
illuminating the brain matter, becoming again the
pinpoint of Light and traveling back the same way,
making the gentle curve, meeting the spine and floating
gently and slowly in the very centre of the hollow of
the spine, passing through all the Lotuses, down to the
very first one. When it has touched the centre of that
Lotus, the four petals close as if to protect something
very precious. Stay quiet and allow to come to you
whatever delicate intuitive perception may want to arise.
Let it happen. If nothing specific happens, that is fine
too. Let yourself be absorbed in that beautiful feeling,
deep peace and harmony.

Do not do this exercise more than once a day. This
will prevent the forcing open of the Lotuses. The
experience of the arising of the Kundalini energy can

take place in such small steps, so gently, as never to upset or jar you into any anxiety. Also, it takes time to reach the ability to concentrate, and to be so alert and yet so relaxed at the same time. Patience and perseverance will lead to an unfolding that can be, if the instructions are followed as given, a very beautiful experience that gives a sense of knowing of the Divine. To pursue the Most High we may have to learn to wait in humility.

reflections

1   Having visualized yourself filled with Light, how do you see yourself? What do you think you would like to change?

2   The ability to focus the mind is key in the healing process. Sit quietly in meditation. Watch the mind for 10 minutes. Then write for 10 minutes. What were you able to recall?

3   In your mind's eye light a candle. Look at it
    for I, 2, up to 5 minutes, excluding all
    thoughts from your mind. What happens
    in your mind when you focus? How do you
    feel?

4   Visualize the Buddha. In one hand he has a
    golden bowl with medicine. See what is in
    it for you.

5   Imagine yourself living life to its fullest.
    What does it look like?

And from this relaxation spreads a peace
and a harmony all over the physical body.
And in this peace and harmony
every cell is relaxed and wide open
to receive more of the great cosmic energy
that sustains it at all times.

relaxation

Did you ever look at your body as if it were a garden? If you take a walk through this unusual garden you may discover something most beautiful and interesting. Get a close look, put attention where needed, and the body pays this kindness back manyfold — in good health, strength and proper functioning.

Most people live in a hectic way, always rushing and racing. Yet, what is accomplished does not match the price because this rushing is too demanding. The way of modern life has made us forget what life really is all about. Have you ever thought what the purpose of your life is? Why are you here? Where did you come from? Where do you go afterward? What is it that makes your heart tick? What is this mysterious thing that we call 'mind'? How does it function? And how does it function in regard to one's body in particular, as one experiences almost all forms of life through it?

Body and mind are in fact closely knit together. It may take time before the body reacts, but when it does so in a disturbing way, it means there has already been a large amount of negative influences coming from the mind. False ideas. False images. They are like woodworms digging tiny little channels into the body. And when these are numerous and get away unchecked, the undermining activity brings a collapse in the physical. First, in those parts that are weak. The breakdown comes gradually, but because we miss being aware of the beginning, we think that the breakdown is sudden.

In the course of time the influences of heat and cold, wind and rain make the hardest rock brittle. So also can the strongest health break down if you don't care for your body. Mental and emotional stress are the influences that work on the human body, breaking resistance down in the course of time. Once the idea of weak health, an allergy or susceptibility is absorbed by the mind, what might be just temporary tiredness from lack of sleep, late hours, etc. is dropped into the mental compartments; the undermining takes place slowly unless we do something about it. Of course, there are many ways to deal with this problem. Periods of rest and quiet are needed where one can be with oneself. We need to have time for ourselves so that we can deal with ourselves properly.

It is necessary to treat one's servant well. Most of us treat the body like a donkey. We demand, often to the point of being unreasonable, that the body perform to the limit of its capacity or even beyond. We may not realize how the restlessness of our thoughts and our ever greedy emotions put the body under stress. The constant desire for pleasure in numerous ways, too numerous to be listed here, needs to be brought under control. The energy and the supply of the cosmic life force can only be abused to a certain point. Nervous exhaustion, sickness, emotional and mental disturbance, even death may result from the lack of self-discipline and in some cases even the lack of awareness for the need of such discipline.

This relaxation exercise is not a magic pill that will allow us to continue to exercise selfishness and self-will at all times. But when we practise awareness in all phases of life, in our daily life and in our contact with people around us, we can unlock the great creative forces that make the individual an outstanding one like a genius or a saint.

Learn to be quiet. To keep the body under control helps us gradually to tune in with others. The greatest joy that we experience is the joy that we can make in the lives of others. Peace and harmony come to us when we bring first peace and harmony to others. There is an ever flowing energy to do all the good for others while we, at the same time, benefit through it too. Who has not experienced an almost miraculous supply of energy when one is concerned for and helping someone else? When we are able to tune in by keeping our minds, our emotions, quiet and under control, we become aware of the needs of others. We develop intuition. And someday our practice will be rewarded with the experience of having tuned in to a cosmic force that gives life abundantly.

practising relaxation

instructions

(You can make a recording of your voice guiding you on this relaxation, or practise with a friend. This allows the relaxation to be more complete. Be sure to guide the mind through the entire body, allowing time for each area of the body to relax. There is also a relaxation CD available from timeless books that guides you through this relaxation.)

Lie down comfortably. Relax all of the body as much as you can. When you breathe, inhale and exhale slowly. Always breathe through the nose. Try to regulate the breath, counting to four. Inhale: one, two, three, four. Exhale: one, two, three, four. Repeat this.

With every incoming breath, let your awareness
expand and with every outgoing breath,
relax more deeply. First, take your mind to
your feet. Let your mind tell your feet,
"Feet relax. Feet relax." The mind observes
the good response from the feet. The feet
and the ankles are very well relaxed indeed.

Now, the mind moves on to the calves. "Calves
relax. Calves relax. Right calf relax. Left
calf relax." Both calves respond very well.
The mind is satisfied that both calves are
very well relaxed.

Go through the entire body in this manner,
moving upward, from the feet to the torso
to the arms and hands to the face and head.
Spend time with each body part, asking
the areas to relax until the body is fully
relaxed from the top of the head to the tip
of the toes.

Now the whole body is marvelously comfortable
and wonderfully relaxed. Your mind, having
done its job, can then relax too.

By regulating your breath, you tune in with this

great rhythm of life, with the great cosmos.
Awareness expands with every incoming
breath. With each outgoing breath the
relaxation deepens.

And from this relaxation spreads a peace and a
harmony all over the physical body. And in
this peace and harmony every cell is relaxed
and wide open to receive more of the great
cosmic energy that sustains it at all times.

Cosmic energy fills every single cell of your
body. Each cell is receiving its share of this
rejuvenating energy. There are healing
forces within each body. Every single cell
may take whatever its need is and even
more. It may store a great supply. Draw
from the abundant supply of energy.
Rejuvenate your whole body. Let the prana
flow into every particle, into every cell.
Accept that you are well. Perfect. Strong.
Each part of your body, every cell, is now
doing its duty. The great force is released
that restores health to you. You have
stepped through the door and into a new

life of well-being. Harmony. Peace and great joy. Remember that this wonderful life force, this prana, will sustain you. The power that creates you sustains you. Move. Live. Be. Find harmony in health.

Take a deep breath. Open your eyes. Feel the energy rush into every cell of your body. Gently move your feet, your hands, your head. Take another deep, deep breath and stretch. Stretch your body all over. Know you are joy. You are peace. You are harmony. You are strength. You are the cosmic atom filled with cosmic energy.

Let your first action be one of gratitude. Be grateful for the gift of your body.

reflections

1   What in your life makes you tense? Where do you feel the tension in your body? Where does the tension start? Where does the relaxation begin?

2   Practise tensing and relaxing. Tense — hands
    and feet, arms and legs, hips and shoulders,
    abdomen and neck. Release the same way.
    Practise until this movement becomes fluid
    like a dance.

3   What resists? What lets go? What part is
    willing? What does surrender mean to you?

4   Pain is a great teacher. Ask yourself: What
    have I learned from my life experiences?
    What are my victories? What is the
    purpose of my life?

5   Visualize a beautiful garden. Remove any
    weeds you see growing. See a wishing well
    and make a wish. Find something of great
    value in your garden. Reflect on the
    meaning of these images you see. What is
    the message?

part three

giving back & giving thanks

the power of healing

The power of healing attracts many people. When one has gained control over the emotions and cultivated them into finer feelings, compassion will be allowed, in due time, to find true expression. When one desires to help because help is needed, rather than for rewards of any kind or for sentimental reasons, this desire has the right basis. It is far more likely that a healing will take place when motivated by noble feelings such as compassion. However, many more aspects come into both success and failure in healing.

When we desire healing for ourselves or others, a few questions come up about the energies involved: Is another person needed to assist healing? Does one have healing power within oneself?

When healing is being considered, the healer must find out how the illness came about. If there has been a continuous violation of some physical principles that has led to the breakdown of health, spiritual healing might be successful only once, if at all. In this case, the person should be properly instructed in taking care of the body and observing the laws under which it will stay healthy. If these are neglected, trust in spiritual healing will be weakened both in the healer and in the one who is ill. It is rare that illness is sudden. It is more likely that preoccupation of the mind with other concerns has been too intense, so that early signs of breakdowns in the body have gone unnoticed. Pain is a great teacher, and illness is often the only way to become truly grateful for health and to see the healthy body as a precious instrument that should be well taken care of.

The attitude of the sick person might be a reason why spiritual healing could not take place. It could fail if there were no will to live, no purpose to life that would give the impetus, or if the purpose had not been grasped, or if the person believed that he or she was too great a sinner to deserve to be healed. Add to this all the psychological advantages of love and attention that go with being ill, and it becomes obvious that there could be little or nothing to promote healing.

So the mental and emotional preparation of ill people is very important. This means that there has to be real concern, not sentiment, to help them to help themselves and to understand some aspects of their predicament. There has to be the cooperation of the desire to be well and the will to live a purposeful life. The healer has to inspire and reinforce these positive thoughts. Emotions play a very important part in the healer and the ill person. There have to be cultivated emotions, feelings of deep gratitude on the part of the person being healed for regained health and on the part of the healer for the privilege of being a channel. Gratitude, being one of the finest of human feelings, plays an important part in the practice and the results.

A healer is a person who has an awareness and perception of those forces that promote healing or correct what is detrimental to health. This awareness makes it possible for the healer to let this energy flow through and direct it to the person who is in need of additional energy that will correct the weakness in the body.

The Divine Light Invocation has the proper combination of all that is necessary to bring about a healing, either spontaneously or by repetition. In the practice of the Divine Light Invocation there has to be a true feeling of compassion and total involvement on the part of the healer, which communicates itself to the sick person. Sometimes psychological problems have to be removed first, and there has to be a healing in the mind before a healing can take place in the body. It is essential that the healer refrain from determining how the healing should take place in order for the Divine Light to flow and set in motion what is necessary for a particular individual. Geographical distance need not be a barrier to healing. The ill person may be 3000 miles away, but our old space/time concept should not prevent us from attempting to help.

At the moment when the needy person is deeply relaxed and in a state of surrender (perhaps because of weakness), he or she becomes receptive and thereby allows the energy to flow and do its work. The healer must observe and understand the state of surrender and deep relaxation. If such a state cannot be achieved while awake, it will naturally take place when the individual falls asleep. In the following two hours when there is a dropping from the conscious level to the unconscious, the body is extremely receptive to repeated suggestions of healing directed toward its own resources. This in itself may lead to healing in some cases.

The efforts described may have to be repeated over a period of from one to three months. It must be realized that in some circumstances healing may not be best for the whole person. The Divine Light cannot be told what to do, but immeasurable benefits will be derived whatever the visible results.

Confidence, trust, hope, the will to live and the view of a goal or purpose in life are some of the basic principles involved in healing. The power of faith and hope should not be underestimated. They are also Energy, which can be increased with concern and involvement through the Divine Light Invocation.

thoughts on gratitude

Humility and gratitude go hand in hand. The feeling of gratitude is an interaction between the mind and the body. Both will benefit from it. Awareness increases so that we become grateful for everything we are given. We have to learn, literally learn, to be grateful for what we receive day by day, simply to balance the criticism that, day by day, we voice because of powerful emotions.

In Buddhist tradition, the aspirant gives 100,000 prostrations to develop humility — a virtue that is thus expressed appropriately through the body. Some people will say, "But I feel I have gratitude and humility, so what is wrong?" You may think and feel you have gratitude, but if you never express it, does it have any meaning?

What can we do to cultivate gratitude and humility?

Eastern traditions use the worship of the guru, which appeals only to some people. But this act of worship has very good psychology behind it. People have an inborn desire to admire and worship. They look for an example after which they can mould themselves. False gods such as success, food, sex, possessions, unproven beliefs and personal convictions are often worshipped until there is an awakening to their emptiness.

Another way to develop gratitude is to truly look at yourself, to see the marvel of this human body and the intricacy of the sensitive organs. Be grateful to have the full use of your senses through which you perceive all that is around you, the world and the beauties of nature. Appreciate the strong body and the state of good health you enjoy.

The mind is always so active scheming to fulfill selfish desires that those shy and modest thoughts of gratitude and humility get pushed into the background. We allow the mind to be stimulated by all sorts of things that often prove to be useless, even detrimental, to our mental and emotional well-being. Thoughtlessly we establish bad habits and allow those to remain, then cry when we experience the pain of our own carelessness. We even interpret this as an unfair destiny, entirely missing the point that we have laid our own traps and we have to take responsibility for those acts. In the course of life, there are many little "miracles," but our hearts are so hardened that we don't pay any attention. Instead we take things for granted. Yet we never allow anyone to take us for granted. When this happens, we protest loudly.

The lengthy prayers and prostrations to all gurus and all Buddhas fulfill a function — the cultivation of the finer feelings and the acknowledgement to those who have paved the way and shared their hard-won experiences with us, helping us to gain insights and to travel the narrow road with faith and endurance, in humility and gratitude.

contact us

timeless books
www.timeless.org

In Canada:
Box 9, Kootenay Bay, BC V0B 1X0
contact@timeless.org
(800) 661-8711

In the United States:
P.O. Box 3543, Spokane, WA 99220-3543
info@timeless.org
(800) 251-9273

about the author

Swami Sivananda Radha (1911–1995) authored more than 10 books on yoga and spirituality, including the seminal *Kundalini Yoga for the West*, and *Radha: Diary of a Woman's Search*. She is the founder of Yasodhara Ashram, and the inspiration for the award-winning yoga magazine, *ascent*. She is known for her practical and passionate teachings, which are an intrinsic part of the yogic tradition in the West. For more information on Swami Sivananda Radha and her teachings, visit www.yasodhara.org